Carly, the Therapy Dog, Goes to Visit

Carly, the Therapy Dog, Goes to Visit

Copyright@2021 Belinda Adams
Illustrations Copyright © 2021 Amara Naybab
Digitally edited by Annie Moore
ISBN: 9781949109665
Library of Congress Control Number: 2021948672
Imprint: Anchor Book Press
440 W. Colifax St., Unit 1132, Palatine, IL 60078
Printed in the United States

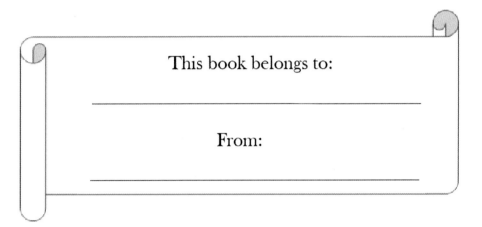

This book belongs to:

_____

From:

_____

Dedication

This book is dedicated to Carly, the therapy dog! Through her unconditional love and acceptance of my students, my students were able to give love and bond with her. With her patience and willingness to sit for hours for little ones to touch and hug her, my students also learned the value of patiently waiting for their turn and loving every single second of their weekly, special time with Carly.

Acknowledgement

I'd like to acknowledge Shelley May, Carly's owner. Without Shelley's commitment to weekly visits with my students, their experience with a therapy dog would not have been possible. In addition to giving us time with Carly, she also developed lasting relationships with each and every one of my students. I know the experience of receiving unconditional love and giving unconditional love to Carly (and Shelley) will be remembered by my students for a lifetime.

It was a Wednesday morning. Carly opened her eyes and sniffed the air, thinking: Why am I awake? I don't smell coffee or bacon.

Yes, I know. Today is visiting day! With a spring in her step, she headed downstairs to greet her humans.

Yes, I was right. There is my special vest I wear when I visit people! Her tail banged excitedly against the kitchen table legs as she thought about what was ahead.

Carly trotted outside with her human to do what all dogs do outside. With a dash, she was back inside, waiting to get ready for her visit.

With a loving smile on her face, her favorite human in the world, Shelley, leaned over and snapped Carly into her special vest. With each 'snap-snap,' Carly's tail wagged faster and faster.

Carly knew there was something special about wearing that red vest with bright white lettering. She could feel how special it was with every hug she received.

Today is a great day! It's the day I visit my favorite small humans at ABC School. They love me there! It's not just the little humans. The big humans make a lot of noise when I'm there, too, Carly thought with a smile.

Carly raced outside to get into the van with her human before driving down the road. Carly watched the scenery and waited for the familiar sight of the school to come into view. Carly started thinking …

As they rode, Carly thought about the hard work of becoming a therapy dog. She had to earn that special vest with the bright white lettering.

There were many practices and visits with lots of strange humans crowded around her. Sometimes, she felt afraid of those unfamiliar faces. Her human, Shelley, was always near. Shelley comforted her, whispering, 'You're doing great, Carly! It's time to visit!'

On one practice, Carly remembered she had to ride in a small box with other humans. There were lots and lots of buttons with lights on the wall. With a skip of her heart, she'd felt the box start to rise up and up and up. At first, she thought it was never going to stop! Finally, it did.

Her human, Shelley, patted her on that long ride upwards. She assured her she was doing great. All of that had been quickly forgotten when she stepped out of the box into a brightly lit hallway filled with small humans.

She smiled as she remembered the tiny, outstretched arms of little humans riding in strange chairs with wheels. A few of those little humans had hard plastic on an arm or leg. Carly heard someone call them 'casts.' Even now, months later, Carly remembered the warm feeling of those tiny arms around her neck giving her big, loving hugs.

Besides the little humans, there were big humans too. Most of them were wearing white and waiting patiently for a chance to pet her.

Then Carly remembered the hardest practice of all. There had been a lot of humans she didn't know. Carly remembered the crashing sound! She was scared because she didn't know what it was. Then she saw the food tray with fried chicken scattered across the floor.

Carly remembered, even now, that her mouth had started to water thinking about that tasty chicken. She had resisted the urge to dash over and gobble it up. Shelley had rubbed her lovingly behind the ears and said, 'Good job, Carly!'

Other practices included outdoor parks with kids running past and other dogs chasing frisbees. She had wanted to join in the fun.

Then she had remembered she was wearing her special vest. Vests are for visits, not playing, she reminded herself, as she sat patiently near her human. Again, Shelley whispered, 'Wonderful job, Carly!'

Sometimes, it was hard to remember she couldn't play with other dogs or chase balls when she was wearing her special vest. Shelley would gently remind her, "It is time to visit now. We can play later."

Her favorite human, Shelley, didn't forget those promises to play later. When the special vest was taken off, Carly chased balls and played with squeaky toys. She had time to run in the back yard with her furry sister, Bella.

With a proud smile, Carly remembered the day she earned the special privilege of being a Registered Therapy Dog. That's the day she earned her bright red vest.

Carly and Shelley had finished all of the practices and Carly had passed with 'flying colors!' Shelley was so happy that day. Carly had a special bone treat that night to celebrate. That had been a great day!

As the van continued to drive towards ABC School, Carly thought about many other visits. She thought about one special visit. No one had been allowed inside. Carly and her human went from window to window, sharing smiles with little humans inside.

It had been a very chilly day. Carly remembered that she hadn't minded the cold. She could feel the love from the little humans as they touched the glass in front of her head.

As the van rounded a corner, Carly could feel her heart beat faster in anticipation. There it was! ABC School! She knew the happiness and hugs that were waiting inside for her.

Carly ran excitedly from one window to the next as her human parked the van. Finally, the door opened for her to jump out.

As Carly bounded into the office, she was greeted by several humans, saying, 'Hello Carly.'

She waited patiently for the human behind the counter to print a name tag for Shelley. Carly didn't have to wait for her name tag. Nope! That's because she had her own, special name badge for the school. It had her name and picture on it. It was almost as if she belonged at ABC School every day.

Everyone in the front of the school liked to say 'Hello' to Carly! They always came to give her a pet or a hug. Carly felt so welcomed at ABC School.

After what was probably half a day of hugs and 'Hello's,' Carly and her human were let out of the office.

Carly knew exactly which direction to go. With a bounce in her steps, she trotted to the door of Room 119.

Carly could hear little voices excitedly saying, 'She's here! Carly's here!' She knew she'd be greeted by several big humans and surrounded by her little humans with warm arms around her neck.

Every little human in Room 119 was different! Yes, they all love me, Carly thought. Each one shows their love in a different way.

One little human loved to read Carly books. Carly was never sure what the story was about. She liked the sound of the little human's voice as he read words and pointed to pages for her to see.

One little human loved to brush Carly's fur with the brush Shelley brought along each week. She showed him how to gently brush her fur. 'To make me beautiful,' thought Carly.

He asked how to take care of Carly. 'With lots of treats,' Carly wanted to bark, if only she could talk. Instead, Carly listened while her human explained about food, water, and baths (which she could really do without, if you asked Carly).

All the little humans loved to touch her soft fur, stroke it and sometimes bury their faces in it. That tickles, Carly thought.

Since Carly had been going to ABC School, she noticed how the little humans were changing. They were getting taller, losing teeth they proudly showed her and Shelley, and learning how to hug her with much more confidence.

Carly remembered one little human in particular. When she had first started coming to ABC school, he had been very reluctant to come close to Carly. Carly wondered why. He needed coaxing by his leader human and Shelley to sit by Carly. Soon, he started touching Carly.

Now, each week, he excitedly raised his hand to ask if he could be first to visit her. 'Gladly,' Carly always thought, happy to see him so excited to see her.

While she visited with her little humans, there were lots of big humans who stopped by to give her a belly scratch or ask for a furry paw.

Carly knew them all! She remembered their scent. She could hear their love for her as they talked fondly to her and stroked her fur.

'Until next week, little humans,' Carly woofed over her shoulder when it was time to go. All the little humans crowded around and waved goodbye to her.

Then she headed out the door toward the van with her human.

Carly was very tired as she jumped into the van to head home. Getting all those hugs can be exhausting, Carly thought to herself. Happily, she laid down in the van. With visions of tiny humans and loving arms dancing in her head, Carly drifted off to sleep.

Meet Carly

Yes, Carly is a real therapy dog! Carly is an English Cream golden retriever (pictured at left with her owner and favorite human, Shelley). She loves her visits, and especially blooms with wagging tail and wide smile when she visits the children in Room 119 at ABC School. She's been known to offer her belly for a great scratching or her paw for those who need a warm handshake. For others, she gladly stretches out and allows them to stroke her fur and talk lovingly to her. Carly is always ready to accept a hug, a pet, a stroke of her fur, or sometimes, just a gaze into her comforting eyes.

Carly's owner, Shelley, says, "Carly is a natural therapy dog. She took to her training and her responsibilities quickly and without hesitation. It was like she was born to be a therapy dog."

Meet the Author

Belinda Adams (pictured left with her para-professional, Becky) is a special education teacher who works with young students with social and emotional needs. For these little people, emotional needs negatively impact their lives and their readiness for learning.

Belinda uses her training as a certified trauma professional and her nearly 20 years of experience working with at-risk students to help her students learn to understand their body's reaction to strong emotions and discover personal strategies that help bring them back to a calm state to become ready to learn. For Belinda, introducing a therapy dog, such as Carly, to her students only made sense. Belinda says, "The weekly addition of Carly allowed the students to experience unconditional love and to give unconditional love."

At right, Belinda and Shelley are pictured as they introduce Carly to the class for the first time. "The students were educated about therapy dogs, how to conduct yourself around a therapy dog, and classroom expectations when Carly was visiting," says Belinda.

Belinda and Shelley not only found joy in bringing these experiences to her students; they've also grown in their understanding of how a regular interaction with a therapy dog enhances the goals of learning social/emotional regulation.

Through it all, Carly's owner, Shelley, will tell you, "I've grown to love these children; to experience their happiness as they tell me their accomplishments and to listen quietly and patiently when they share their deepest trauma with me while visiting Carly. I'm so glad we could experience this and learn so much about the power of a therapy dog in a specialized classroom."

At left, Carly is greeted by a student in Belinda's class. "Each week, the students' reactions when they saw Carly were very expressive and emotional," says Belinda.

About the Illustrator

Amara Naybab is a professional artist who specializes in picture books for children. Her creativity and artistic skills are highly rated. She loves to draw and works with the author to be sure the book is something children will love to read time and again. Her illustrations have a magic touch that children find  fascinating. She is a top rated African American illustrator.

Therapy Dogs and the Classroom

"There are no words to thoroughly describe the love generated when a young child shares the experience of a therapy dog in the classroom," says author Belinda Adams. "There's a calm that comes over them, a peacefulness and a realization that they are the recipient of a special love and bond."

According to a study published by the National Institute of Health, a therapy dog in the classroom "promotes a positive mood and provides significant anti-stress effects on the body. In fact, the simple act of petting a dog has the effect of lowering blood pressure and heart rate" (NIH, Weareteachers.com). In Belinda's classroom especially, where students struggle with social and emotional balance, the addition of a therapy dog in the classroom reduces feelings of anxiety and depression that allow their brains to get ready for learning. In particular to students struggling with emotional dysregulation, a classroom therapy dog "builds trust and trustworthiness in children and help them develop a greater capacity for empathy" (NIH, Weareteachers.com).

In addition to the social/emotional benefits, the NIH study also supported that classroom therapy dogs "improve students' reading skills, stimulates memory, and problem-solving skills and even optimizes executive functioning skills" (NIH, Weareteachers.com).

Belinda doesn't need to re-read the research. She's witnessed all of these benefits on a firsthand basis. Without a doubt, the regular presence of a therapy dog in her classroom has provided her students with experiences and opportunities to grow socially, emotionally, and cognitively.

More Books by Belinda Adams

Belinda Adams has degrees in elementary education, special education and psychology. She's worked with at risk children for the past 17 years. Her books focus primarily on her experiences in teaching students with varying needs, including strategies and data-driven approaches for teachers and parents. She is also the author of two children's books. Belinda's book titles include:

The first and second in The Adventures of Super Dino Boy Series-

Mom's Gift:
> There's No Problem Too Big for
> Mom & Me

I'm Different & That's OK with Me!

Can You See Me?
Using Understanding to Help Students of Poverty Feel Seen, Heard & Valued in the Classroom

Can You See Me Yet? There is More to Learn
> Using Understanding to Help Students of Poverty Feel
> Seen, Heard & Valued in the Classroom

Don't Look Too Closely:
> What Children of Trauma are Hiding and How You Can
> Be the Difference for Them

If Only She Knew:
> Engaging the Whole Student with Trauma in Mind

Parents REACH for Success:
  4 Strategies to Give Your Child the Growth Mindset
    for School Success

REACH for Success:
  4 Strategies to Positively Impact Your Classroom

There's More to Me Than She Can See:
  Engaging the Whole Student with Trauma in Mind

Why Math? Mental Anguish to Humanity:
  Engaging At-Risk Students in Math and Science When
the Teacher Hates Teaching It

Made in the USA
Monee, IL
22 November 2021

82710727R00021